A handbook for babysitters and parents

Written for British Red Cross Youth
by Alexandra Studd.

British Red Cross

National H

9 Grosvenor Crescent London SW1X 7EJ
Telephone 071-235 5454 Fax 071-235 7447
A Registered Charity

Acknowledgements

With special thanks to:

Jennie Lindon
of People Consulting

Chris Hillier and Jean Lee
of British Red Cross –
Somerset Branch

Designed by John Brown

Cartoons by Martin Shovel

Contents

Foreword

The role of a babysitter is a very responsible and often underestimated one; so is the role of a parent or guardian who "employs" a young person as a babysitter. In producing this handbook, British Red Cross Youth aims to make babysitters, parents and guardians more aware of these responsibilities while providing babysitters with advice and easy-to-access guidelines on various aspects of babysitting including basic first aid, responding to emergencies and everyday child care.

I hope that by using this handbook, young people will feel more confident about babysitting and that parents or guardians will feel more confident about leaving their children with babysitters.

Andrew Case
Head of Youth

So why do you need a handbook?

Young children and babies are frequently left in the temporary care of teenagers. It happens every night of the week in households all over the UK. It's known as babysitting.

Finding and using a babysitter is a basic need for many parents.
A babysitter may enable parents to attend an evening class, to go late night shopping or to enjoy an evening out with friends. Relatives sometimes take over, but those parents who cannot get relatives to babysit, often turn to the teenage children of friends and neighbours.

Babysitters are sometimes expected to cope in less than ideal circumstances. Perhaps parents have arranged for a babysitter to look after two children and at the last minute the neighbours leave two more. Even the most experienced adult would be worried by some of the situations faced by babysitters. No matter how responsible or expert the babysitter, emergency situations involving the health and welfare of babies and young children, can and do arise.

This handbook has been written in order to help babysitters prepare for the responsibilities of their roles and to help them understand what it is they should expect from a "sitting" session. Looking after children requires a wide range of skills and knowledge. The handbook offers advice for babysitters on different aspects of babysitting including basic child care, coping with accidents and first aid. The handbook is also intended as a resource for parents who use babysitters, raising parents' awareness of their own responsibilities and helping them understand what they might reasonably expect from a babysitter. It is hoped that both new and experienced babysitters, as well as parents, will find the handbook an invaluable guide.

A "parent" or the "parents" are not always the biological mother or father of the child in question. For the purposes of this handbook the use of the word "parent" or "parents" means the adult or adults with parental responsibility for the infant or child.

The author has deliberately alternated the use of "he" and "she" when referring to a parent, a babysitter or to the infant or child in

"even the most experienced adult would be worried by some of the situations faced by babysitters"

the babysitter's care. The author has also varied the use of the words "baby", "infant", "child" and "children".

The British Red Cross co-ordinates Babysitters' Training Programmes throughout the United Kingdom. The training programmes are aimed at young people wishing to prepare themselves for their roles and responsibilities as babysitters. The training provides education in basic home safety, first aid and child care through practical demonstrations and role play. This handbook is no substitute for essential awareness training.

Find out more about the Babysitters' Training Programme by, in the first instance, contacting your school, college or group and showing them this booklet. Ask them to consider running the Programme. They should contact their local county British Red Cross Branch for further details. Failing that, contact the local county British Red Cross Branch yourself. They should be able to put you in contact with someone who is running the Programme nearby. You will find the telephone number and address in your local directory.

What is babysitting?

Babysitting is a flexible arrangement. One family's requirements will not necessarily match those of another; one babysitting session will vary from the next. One night you might not see the children except when checking on them during the evening; the next night you might try all evening to settle the baby.

As a babysitter your responsibilities will be varied. You might be expected to:

Babysitting is looking after children in their own home in the temporary absence of their parents, usually in the evening but sometimes for short periods during the day. A babysitter must never care for children in her own home or on any other premises. This arrangement is known as childminding and is strictly controlled by law. Babysitting is a private arrangement made between the babysitter and parent; hours, fees and what is expected of the babysitter need to be agreed by both parties.

- Settle the children into bed.
- Comfort and reassure a child.
- Read or play games with a child until it is time for bed.

As a general rule babysitting shouldn't involve the personal care of the children. Unless previously arranged, babies and young children should already be bathed, fed and ready for bed. However, parents may allow older children to take some responsibility for doing these things themselves.

You are not normally responsible for any domestic chores, except tidying/washing up after yourself.

"you are not normally responsible for any domestic chores, except tidying/washing up after yourself"

The law and babysitting

There are no laws in the United Kingdom specifically concerned with babysitting. There are no legal restrictions on who may offer themselves or be chosen by a parent as a babysitter. However, the British Red Cross would like to emphasise the importance of parents exercising care and discretion when choosing a babysitter. Their choice should be based upon a number of factors including most importantly knowledge of their own child/children and of the babysitter. In terms of liability, when leaving a child in the care of a babysitter, a parent remains potentially liable. However, any babysitter who endangers a child's health or safety, may also be liable.

There is no law which states at what age it is legal for a young person to babysit; parents must decide whether someone is old enough to babysit. The British Red Cross, as a responsible organisation, considers it undesirable to leave a child in the care of someone under the age of 14. While age is by no means the only factor to take into account, babysitters under this age may simply lack the life experience to be able to take on the required responsibilities.

For further information contact The Children's Legal Centre on 071-359 6261.

Babysitters' rights

As a babysitter you have the right to:

- Decide which families you "sit" for.
- Negotiate a fair and reasonable "deal" (fee, hours etc.) with parents.
- Discuss and negotiate changes regarding any aspects of babysitting with which you are uncomfortable.

Babysitters' responsibilities

Parents have trusted you with the safety and well-being of their children, temporarily left in your care. As a babysitter, you have responsibilities to both the parents and the children.

Maybe you've had several strange telephone calls, the electricity fuses or the baby won't stop crying. If a crisis or worrying situation arises, never feel you have to continue to cope on your own. If you're unsure or unhappy about anything it is advisable to seek help. Use one of the contact numbers you have been given (see pages 34-35). Never risk your own safety or that of the children in your care. It is reasonable for the parents to expect you to act in a responsible manner.

The following is a list of basic responsibilities:

- Give parents as much warning of cancellation as possible. If you feel unwell, ring the parents immediately. Give them time to find another babysitter.
- Don't babysit if you are ill. You won't babysit to the best of your ability. You might pass on your illness to the children.
- Always tell your own parents the name, address and telephone number of the family for whom you are babysitting. Tell them how you are getting home and what time you expect to be back. If the children's parents ring you to say they will be home late, let someone at your own home know of the change in plans.
- Arrive alert, sober and in an appropriate frame of mind to assume your responsibilities.
- Arrive in plenty of time to talk to the parents and to write down details relevant to the babysitting session.
- Ensure parents leave their own contact number and two other contact numbers in case of an emergency.
- Stay in the home all the time the parents are out.
- Stay awake all the time you are babysitting (unless it has previously been arranged that you are staying the night).
- Nothing must interfere with your duties as a babysitter. If at any time the children need you, your

"nothing must interfere with your duties as a babysitter"

homework must be put aside or the television turned off while you care for them.

- Don't smoke or drink. Smoking or drinking could endanger a child's health and safety.
- Make sure that any heater or fire is kept guarded.
- If you are listening to music or watching television make sure you can hear the children above the volume. Keep the baby alarm on and the door of the room ajar.
- Make a quiet check on babies every half hour and on older children every hour.

- Only use the telephone in a crisis or emergency. Parents must be able to contact you at any moment.
- Respect prior agreements made with parents about the use of facilities (TV/video, food and drink etc.).
- Unless previously agreed and arranged, do not invite or allow your own friends to come round.
- Don't rummage through drawers or cupboards while the parents are out. Respect the privacy of their home.
- Maintain the security of the home to the best of your ability (see 'What about Security?' on page 24).
- Leave the home as it was when you arrived (toys are put away, your dirty coffee mug is washed up etc.).
- For your own safety, never advertise your services as a babysitter.

"only use the telephone in a crisis"

Parents' rights

As a parent you have the right to:

- Decide who babysits for you.
- Tackle unexpected or unacceptable behaviour by a babysitter.
- Decide you do not want to use the babysitter again.

Parents' responsibilities

"a babysitter is trusted with your children not with any domestic chores"

As a parent it is your responsibility to satisfy yourself that a babysitter is suitable and capable of being trusted with your children.

Be clear about your expectations of a babysitter - how do you expect him to treat your home, what facilities can he use, how should he deal with any misbehaviour from the child? Irritations over food being eaten, the stereo being used or friends coming by uninvited are easily dealt with by discussing them before they arise.

As a parent it is your responsibility to:

- Engage a responsible, trustworthy and reliable babysitter who will put the safety and welfare of the children before anything else.

- Agree payment and sitting hours in advance. Pay the babysitter in full at the end of the evening.
- Cancel the babysitter if a child is ill. It is not fair to expect a babysitter to nurse your child. If a child has recently been unwell, tell the babysitter.

- Give an approximation to the nearest hour of the time you will return.
- Answer all the questions a babysitter might ask.
- Leave written instructions about any medication that the babysitter is required to give.
- Leave specific advice about a child who's been particularly difficult with babysitters in the past (e.g. who may refuse to go to bed).
- Leave relevant contact and emergency telephone numbers.
- Leave the name and telephone number of the children's doctor.
- If at all possible write down an address and telephone number where you are contactable during the course of the evening.
- Point out the rooms where the children are sleeping.
- Show the babysitter any fire exit.
- Inform the babysitter if you are going to arrive home later than expected.
- Ensure the babysitter arrives home safely.

To be agreed beforehand.....

It is advisable to sort out some practicalities before the "sit". This prevents confusion or embarrassment occurring later.

The fee

Always agree a fee before you "sit" At the same time, establish the approximate number of babysitting hours. Don't ever leave a discussion on payment until the end of the "sit".

Before negotiating your fee, ask around and find out the local going rate. Do babysitters charge by the hour or by the evening? Is there an extra charge after midnight? Is it usual to charge extra if the babysitter is looking after more than a particular number of children?

People often get embarrassed talking about money. Before you discuss babysitting with any parent, know in your mind what fee you expect. If a parent wants to negotiate your fee, decide how low you are prepared to go; know your own minimum. Work out in advance what you are going to say to a parent. A parent who seldom uses a babysitter may ask you how much you expect to receive for an evening's babysitting. Reassure parents that the fee you charge is in line with local babysitting rates or is the same as you are paid by other families.

Points to consider

- Give parents plenty of warning if you are increasing your fees.
- Be clear about your minimum charge, particularly if you are being paid by the hour.
- If at all possible, get your fee confirmed in writing. This will help avoid misunderstandings.
- If a parent arrives home late, you should receive an extra fee for the babysitting time over and above what was arranged.
- If the "sit" includes sleeping at the children's home, a separate fee should be negotiated.

Use of facilities

It should be agreed what food and drink a babysitter can help themselves to. Depending on the time of day the "sit" is taking place, should you eat before you arrive or will a meal be provided? Parents should demonstrate how any cooking equipment (oven, microwave etc.) operates, if appropriate. Do parents mind if you watch the television or a video, or listen to music? How does the equipment operate? Can you turn the heating on or off / up or down? If so, how?

Arrangements for getting home

It should be ensured that you get home safely. You should be walked home, put in a taxi or driven home by someone with whom you are comfortable to drive.

If it is a very late "sit" and it is convenient or possible, arrangements should be made for you to stay the night. This arrangement should be made in advance and agreed with your own parents.

Questions every babysitter should ask!

Before babysitting for a new family, it is advisable to:

- Visit the home (for your own safety, take a parent along with you). Take a list of questions with you.
- Meet the parents and the children.

Most of the following questions only need to be asked at this first meeting. Keep written records about each family – names of children, dates of birth, allergies etc. Take the appropriate notes with you every time you babysit. The questions below are a general guide. If you are a parent you may find the questions a useful reminder of things you need to tell your babysitter at the first meeting. Details can be recorded on the information sheet found at the end of this handbook.

Be prepared

- How many children are you babysitting?
- What are the children's names?
- What are the children's ages?

Know the children's routines

- What time do the children go to bed?
- Are the children allowed to watch television? If so, when and what?
- Do the children have a snack/ drink before they go to bed? If so, what?
- Should younger children be settled into bed by the babysitter or will they settle themselves down?
- Are they allowed to read for a while?

- Are younger children read a bedtime story? Is it read to them in bed or elsewhere in the home?
- What time are lights turned out? Should any lights be left on?
- Is the bedroom door left ajar or closed?

Settling a baby in bed

Does the parent:

- Lay the baby on his back or side?
- Give the baby a drink before he goes to bed?
- Change the baby's nappy?

Children's health

- Is there anything you need to know about the health of the children?
- If the parents are aware of a specific condition, are there any likely situations with which you need to be able to cope?
- Do the children have any allergies to food/drink or medication, e.g. peanuts, penicillin?
- Do any of the children suffer from asthma? If so, what triggers an attack? Are there any danger signs you can watch out for which are symptoms of an impending attack? How should you cope?

"are the children read a bedtime story?"

Where are things kept?

- Where is the first aid equipment kept?
- Where are nappies, change of clothes, change of bedding stored?
- Where are candles/torches kept in case of a power cut or the electricity fusing?

Safety

- Know the layout of the entire home before the parents go out. Ask them to show you around.
- Where are any telephones situated? You might need a telephone in a hurry. If there is no telephone, what are the arrangements for contacting the parents or any other contacts?
- Does the home have an alarm? If so, is there a "panic button" you can press?
- Where is the electricity fusebox? Check that you know how to switch the power off in case of the electricity fusing.

Other useful information

It is sensible and advisable for the babysitter and parent to discuss the way in which parents normally respond to situations that may arise during the "sit".

It is a good idea to find out whether a child regularly:

- Wakes up during the night.
- Suffers from nightmares/sleepwalking.
- Misbehaves or is unhappy when left with a babysitter.

If so, parents should make it clear to the babysitter how they should respond.

If a baby wakes and cries should you leave the baby for a while to see if he will settle? Should you pick him up? If so, how do the parents normally hold him? Should you give him a bottle? If so, what is the procedure for preparing a bottle and giving it to the baby? Should you check and change the baby's nappy?

Do any of the children have "comforters" or special toys that are reassuring to them?

If a child ever misbehaves when left with babysitters, how should you deal with the situation?

"does the child suffer from nightmares/sleepwalking?"

Information for emergencies

- Ask the parents to leave the telephone numbers and addresses of at least two neighbours/friends/relatives to contact in case of a crisis.
- Make a note of at least two emergency telephone numbers; the family doctor/the local hospital/the local police station.
- Ask the parents to write down the full address and telephone number of the home in which you are sitting. Clear instructions on how to get to the home should be written down for you to direct the emergency services should help be needed.
- Make sure you know the procedure for dialing 999; see page 35 for details.

IN CASE OF EMERGENCY
DIAL 999

What about security?

A babysitter needs to maintain the security of the home, for his own safety as well as for that of the children:

- Check that doors are locked but that the keys are immediately accessible.
- Make sure the door is on a safety chain if there is one.
- Don't leave windows open unless essential for ventilation purposes.
- Are the parents expecting any callers in person or on the telephone?
- Check that light switches work.

Answering the door

- If there is a safety chain, check it is on.
- Ask who it is (if there is no safety chain, shout through the door) and find out what they want.
- **Do not open the door to any stranger.**
- If someone claims to be a friend, neighbour or relative, explain that for safety reasons you can't let them in. Ask them to come back when the parents are in. **Do not let them in.**

Answering the telephone

Answer the telephone sensibly. Inform the caller that the person they want is temporarily out but will return the call later. Ask if you can take down a name, number and any message. Avoid saying you are the babysitter; "family friend" might be better. Be brief and businesslike.

If the home has an answer machine, you could listen each time the telephone rings and pick it up only when you recognise the parent's or your own parent's voice.

If you get any strange phone calls or the same person calls more than twice, contact the parents if possible. Otherwise phone the local police station, one of the other contact numbers or your own parents. If you see anyone acting suspiciously outside the home or you are frightened by any other situation that arises, dial 999 and ask for the police operator.

For further information on safety matters, contact your Crime Prevention Officer through your local Police Station or the Partnership and Community Safety Branch at New Scotland Yard.

Having fun!

Parents ask you to babysit because they want a responsible person in the home to care for their children while they are temporarily out. You are needed in case of an emergency such as fire, sickness or accidents. You are also needed to play with or provide company for the children. You may be babysitting for children of different ages and their needs will be different. They may need you to entertain them or to help them with their homework. A home with children is likely to be equipped with appropriate playthings and books. Find out where toys and books are kept.

Most younger children have an interest in drawing, writing, looking at pictures in books and magazines, and listening to stories. Try and bring along a few surprises; this will make your job easier. Towards bedtime play should get quieter; you want them to go to bed in a calm frame of mind.

Clearing up afterwards

Involve the children in tidying up. Make it a competition - "I bet I can clear this up before you can put your puzzle away". Thank them for helping.

"towards bedtime play should get quieter"

What happens if.....?

You are unhappy or unsure about babysitting for a particular family?

Discuss the situation with someone who might be able to advise you - maybe a friend who has worked for the same family. Talk to your own parents. Don't return to a family who does not respect your rights as a babysitter. Trust your instincts.

You feel unhappy or uncomfortable about a situation that arises while you are babysitting?

Depending on the extent to which you feel unhappy or uncomfortable, either phone your parents, the child's parents if they are contactable or one of the other contacts the parents have given you. If you feel very uncomfortable about a situation, (e.g. you are receiving strange phonecalls) have a parent or friend come over if you cannot contact the child's parents to ask them to come home.

You don't like babysitting at short notice but find it difficult to say you can't "sit" when you are in fact free for the evening?

Be ready with a prepared answer. This will save you getting embarrassed.

You are unhappy to be driven home by the parent who is driving?

Suggest they call you a taxi (at their expense) or telephone a friend or your own parents and request that they collect you. Be assertive.

The baby starts crying and won't stop?

All healthy babies cry from time to time, usually because they are hungry or thirsty, their nappy needs changing or they are uncomfortable. Try any one or all of the following:

- Offer a bottle of milk, water or juice, depending on the parents' advice.
- Pick the baby up (make sure you support the baby's head and neck).
- Gently rock the baby.
- Change the nappy (make sure you know how).

A child misbehaves?

This should have been discussed with the parents beforehand. In general though:

- Be firm to start with and clear about what you want them to do.
- Coming to a compromise is preferable to confrontation.
- Try not to alter the parents' routines.

If a child does misbehave tell the parents on their return. Explain exactly what happened at what time. Be honest. How did it start? How did you cope? What would the parents have done in this situation? This will help you with ideas for the future.

A parent makes inappropriate remarks or makes over-friendly or physical advances?

Tell your parents. Don't babysit for the family again. Never compromise your own safety.

Parents do not pay the full amount for the evening claiming they have no change or are short of change?

Ask the parents to make a note that they owe you money, make a note of this yourself. Remind the parents that they owe you this money next time you babysit. If it happens again say to the parents you find it embarrassing asking them for the money you are owed. Can they make sure they pay you in full on the evening?

Coping with accidents and illness

"if anything should go wrong you must keep calm"

Fortunately most babysitting sessions end happily and nothing goes wrong. However, if anything should go wrong you must keep calm and know what to do. Above all don't panic.

Prevent accidents happening by noting potential hazards in the home. Remove toys from stairways, ensure that fires are guarded etc.

When children are left alone you cannot prevent them getting into mischief. Always supervise the children you are babysitting, especially babies and toddlers who should always be in the same room as you except when they are sleeping. Older children may be allowed to go unsupervised for short periods of time.

Prompt action in cases of injury and illness can prevent a worse situation happening. Make a note of any accident that happens, what happened at what time and how you coped. Inform the parents immediately on their return.

Accidental injuries

All children suffer from occasional bumps, bruises, cuts and grazes. A plaster applied to superficial injuries will often calm or reassure even the most distressed child. However, check in advance whether the child has a reaction to plasters, if so identify what to use instead.

Before applying any dressing, always make sure the area to be covered is clean and dry, by washing under flowing water and gently drying with a clean unfluffy cloth.

Illness

You should not be asked to babysit if a child is unwell. However, babies and young children can become ill very quickly. Watch out for a child who seems abnormally unhappy, is crying a lot, or complains of feeling unwell. The infant or child might be:

- Hot and sweaty to touch.
- Vomiting.
- Suffering from diarrhoea.
- Showing signs of a rash.
- Crying constantly.
- Complaining of pain.

If there are indications of any of the above it is important that you take prompt action. Contact the parents and ask them to return home. If you cannot contact the parents use one of the contact numbers you have been given or call the doctor and ask her to make a home visit.

Babysitters should never give any form of treatment to a baby or child unless it is part of a course and the parent has written down instructions for its use.

In the event of an emergency:

- Call 999.
- Call the child's parent if they are contactable; if not, call the second emergency contact or your own parents.
- While waiting for help, keep the injured child comfortable, talk to and reassure him.
- Reassure any other children.

Basic first aid

If you are a babysitter it is important that you have some basic first aid skills. "The Basics of Babysitting" Babysitters' Training Programme provides practical experience in first aid including infant and child resuscitation procedures. To find out more about the training courses contact your local county Branch of the British Red Cross.

In cases of severe accident or injury never be afraid to call an ambulance. They will always give you valuable advice.

Below are a few tips for minor first aid should you need them. In any situation it is important that you keep calm.

Wounds

Control bleeding by applying gentle pressure to the wound either with your own clean hand or with a clean unfluffy cloth. Raise the injured part. If an object is embedded in the wound, do not try to remove it. Apply firm pressure on either side and raise the injured part.

Falls

If a child has fallen badly don't panic, you need to reassure the child so that he calms down. Do not move the child. Keep him warm by covering with a blanket. Call for an ambulance.

Burns and scalds

Avoid carrying anything hot (drink/food) while the children are still up.

To treat a burn or scald keep the injured part under cold water for at least ten minutes. Cover with a clean, dry cloth, or if not available a clean handkerchief, pillowcase or cling film. Never apply a plaster or use fluffy material or cotton wool. If the skin is badly burnt, blistered, has turned white, brown, or charred, you need emergency help.

Nosebleeds

Sit the child down with his head well forward. Ask him to breathe through his mouth. Pinch the nose just below the bridge for 10 minutes. Provide a cloth for the child to dribble into but ask him not to speak, swallow, cough, spit or sniff as he will disturb the blood clots. If the nose continues to bleed after 30 minutes you need emergency help.

Choking

Encourage the child to cough. If choking continues lean the child forward and give firm slaps to the back between the shoulder blades. If the cause of choking is still not dislodged call an ambulance.

Swallowing poison

Do not give the child anything to drink. **Dial 999 immediately** to get the child to hospital, call the parents. If possible ensure the ambulance staff are given a sample of what the child has swallowed as well as the container it came from.

IN CASE OF EMERGENCY
DIAL 999

In the event of a fire

SMOKE AND FIRE KILL

Don't ever put yourself or the children at risk. If in doubt get everyone out.

- Know your fire escape options. How would you escape a fire upstairs, downstairs, at the back or the front of the home? How would you get to the children and how would you get them out of the home if there was a fire?
- Check whether there are any fire blankets or extinguishers. Where are they kept? Are there any built-in fire exits?

Action to take in case of a fire

- If there is a fire in the home and you have any doubts about extinguishing it, **GET OUT** immediately. Take the children with you.
- Alert the neighbours.
- Dial 999.
- Don't return to the home for anything.

"**GET OUT** immediately. Take the children with you."

If something on the cooker catches fire smother the flames using a damp tea towel or hand towel. **Do not remove this.** Turn off the electricity/gas. **Never** pour water on a fat fire or electrical fire. If you have to cook with oil while babysitting, be extremely careful.

- On a small fire use a fire blanket or fire extinguisher if available.
- If clothing catches fire, smother the flames with a coat or a blanket.

If you are trapped by fire or smoke, move to the room farthest from the fire. Block all the gaps around the doors with clothes and bedding. Shout for help from a window. Don't open the window too far. Always crawl if there is a lot of smoke, there is clearer air near the floor.

IN CASE OF ANY FIRE, HOWEVER SMALL, DIAL 999

These pages can be photocopied for use by the babysitter and the parents. The information written on it is confidential.

Information sheet for babysitters and parents

Name of Parents:

____

Full Address: ____________________

____

____

____

____

____

Telephone Number:

____

Names of Children, Dates of Birth and Ages:

____

____

____

____

____

____

____

Children's Allergies:

____

____

____

Important Information About Children: (bedtimes, interests, toys, comforters, favourite drinks etc.)

____

____

____

____

____

____

____

____

____

____

____

____

____

____

____

____

____

____

____

____

____

____

Contact numbers and addresses in case of an emergency:
(friends, neighbours or relatives)

1. ______________________________

____

____

____

____

2. ______________________________

____

____

____

____

3. ______________________________

____

____

____

____

Family Doctor: ______________________

Local Police: ______________________

Local Hospital: ______________________

____

____

____

____

IN CASE OF EMERGENCY DIAL 999

Address, Telephone Number and Clear Directions to House

____

____

____

____

____

____

____

____

____

____

____

DIALING 999

- Lift the handset, dial 999.
- When the operator answers, listen carefully to what is being asked.
- Say which emergency service you require (fire, police, ambulance).
- Say what telephone number you are calling from.
- When you are through to the emergency service tell them:
  - What the trouble is.
  - Where the trouble is (address and postcode).
  - Your telephone number.
- Don't hang up until the emergency service asks you to do so.

The Fundamental Principles of the International Red Cross and Red Crescent Movement

Humanity

The International Red Cross and Red Crescent Movement, born of a desire to bring assistance without discrimination to the wounded on the battlefield, endeavours, in its international and national capacity, to prevent and alleviate human suffering wherever it may be found. Its purpose is to protect life and health and to ensure respect for the human being. It promotes mutual understanding, friendship, co-operation and lasting peace amongst all peoples.

Impartiality

It makes no discrimination as to nationality, race, religious beliefs, class or political opinions. It endeavours to relieve the suffering of individuals, being guided solely by their needs, and to give priority to the most urgent cases of distress.

Neutrality

In order to continue to enjoy the confidence of all, the Movement may not take sides in hostilities or engage at any time in controversies of a political, racial, religious or eological nature.

Independence

The Movement is independent. The National Societies, while auxiliaries in the humanitarian services of their governments and subject to the laws of their respective countries, must always maintain their autonomy so that they may be able at all times to act in accordance with the principles of the Movement.

Voluntary service

It is a voluntary relief movement not prompted in any manner by desire for gain.

Unity

There can be only one Red Cross or one Red Crescent Society in any one country. It must be open to all. It must carry on its humanitarian work throughout its territory.

Universality

The International Red Cross and Red Crescent Movement, in which all Societies have equal status and share equal responsibilities and duties in helping each other, is worldwide.